Trolls
and their relatives

In the beginning was darkness . . . . .

. . . and in darkness trolls are born.

For millions of years <u>Norway</u>
was covered in darkness, snow and ice.
When, finally, the darkness lifted
and most of the snow and ice
had melted away . . . .

. . . the <u>trolls</u> were there.

They were still there when the first <u>Norwegian</u> came strolling along with his belongings.

He found them in different colours, shapes and sizes:

Big ones . . . ,

tall ones . . . ,

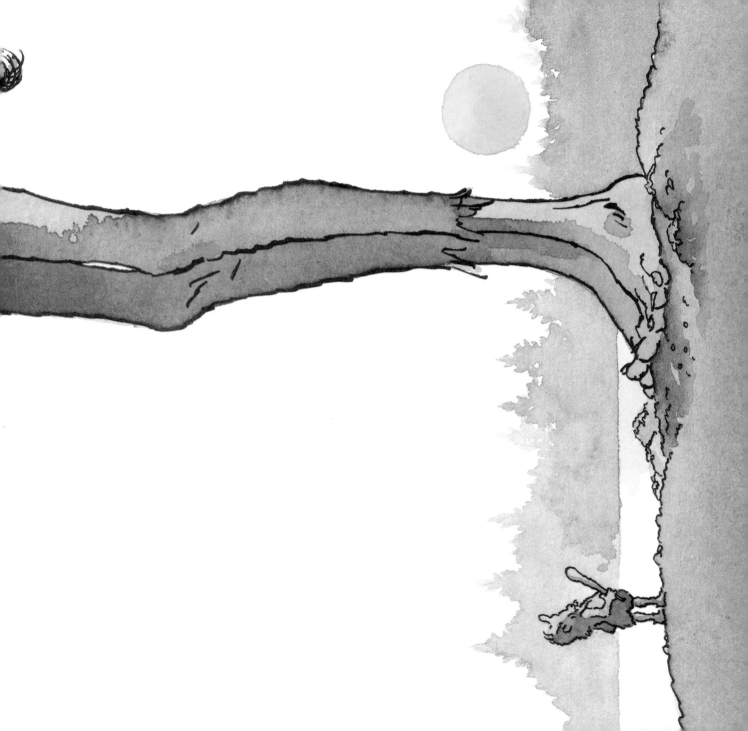

standard sized and
mini ones . . .;

. . . all with tails and only 8 fingers and 8 toes.

At first the Norwegians were not too particular about housing; they lived in caves. But as the trolls too preferred to live inside the mountains, they had to fight the Norwegians for it . . .

Now and then the Norwegians won . . .

...but just as often they lost.

Fairly soon the Norwegians discovered
that the trolls always rule at night,
with a free go at any human soul who
dares to wander around in the darkness . . .

But mostly,
humans rule the day, and
every troll caught by the
sunshine is turned
into stone,
and bursts.
The remains
of unfortunate trolls can
be seen all over the
place in Norway.

As time went on the Norwegians turned into <u>Vikings.</u>
Brave people, their greatest fun drinking mead…

. . . and chopping heads off.

The Vikings were great sea-faring people, roaming all over the oceans.

(Short break for a family tale:)
A sea-faring Viking, Eirik the Red, was born some time ago a few miles outside a small Norwegian town called Stavanger.

We are not sure why he was called the Red, if it was because of his red hair, or his red complexion due to bad temper and drinking too much mead, or other peoples' blood spilt on him, or a combination of all.

He and his father had a nasty habit of cutting down other people. His father cut down someone in Norway, thus had to flee that country. Eirik went with him. They went to Iceland, where Eirik in due time cut down some more people. He had to flee again, but did not know where to go. So he had to discover Greenland, did so, and settled there.

His son, Leiv Eirik-son, found Greenland a little chilly in the winter, so he gathered his men and sailed south. Down south he discovered Wineland the Good, later called America, and settled there for some time.

But as stories go, he and his men invited the native girls for a ride in their boat, the native boys went mad and nasty, and that was the end of that discovery. (End of family tale.)

The Vikings dreaded only one thing,
<u>Draugen</u>, a seacousin of the land troll . . .

. . . and maybe his brother, <u>Nøkken</u>,
who lives in the slimy, dark, bottomless
pools . . .

. . or his other brother, <u>Fossegrimen</u>, who lives in the waterfalls. He is the musical one of the bunch, and the one who teaches the fiddle players of Norwegian folklore how to play their tunes. But to do so they have to offer him a goat, the fatter the better.

Have you ever wondered where the squeaky noise of the Norwegian folklore-fiddle comes from?

Now you know.

It's from the goat.

As time went on, some very brave monks came over from England to bring Christianity to the Vikings. But knowing their reputation, they didn't believe they could convert them only with godliness, so they brought with them a rather sinister character and planned to use him to scare Christianity into the Vikings.

But the Norwegians took this sinister character to their bosom, named him <u>Old Erik</u>, dressed him up as an official, (tax collector?) and in this way he wanders around collecting souls. He is easily recognizable, having horns and beard like a goat, one normal foot and one cloven hoof. He is believed to be closely related to the trolls, maybe the master of them all.

The Norwegians try to cheat and fool Old Erik as often as they can.

(Typical story)

A Norwegian boy was sitting by the roadside cracking nuts. Just as he found a worm-eaten one, Old Erik came wandering along.

'Is it true what people say about you?' the boy asked Old Erik, 'that you can make yourself so small that you can creep into this nut here through this tiny worm-hole?' Old Erik proudly said yes, and did so. Quickly, the boy put a twig in the hole. He then went to the blacksmith and asked him to crack the nut for him. The blacksmith put the nut on the anvil, took his smallest hammer and knocked the nut very gently. No result. Then he took a slightly bigger hammer, knocked still gently. No result. Then he took a middle-sized hammer, knocked not so gently. No result. Then he took a big hammer, knocked hard. No result. Then the blacksmith got real mad, grabbed his biggest hammer and banged down on the nut with all his might. Results! The nut cracked and with a tremendous bang Old Erik and half the smithy roof went sky-high. Said the stunned blacksmith: 'I mean the devil himself was in that nut.'

He sure was.

(End of typical story)

But usually Old Erik gets what he is after.

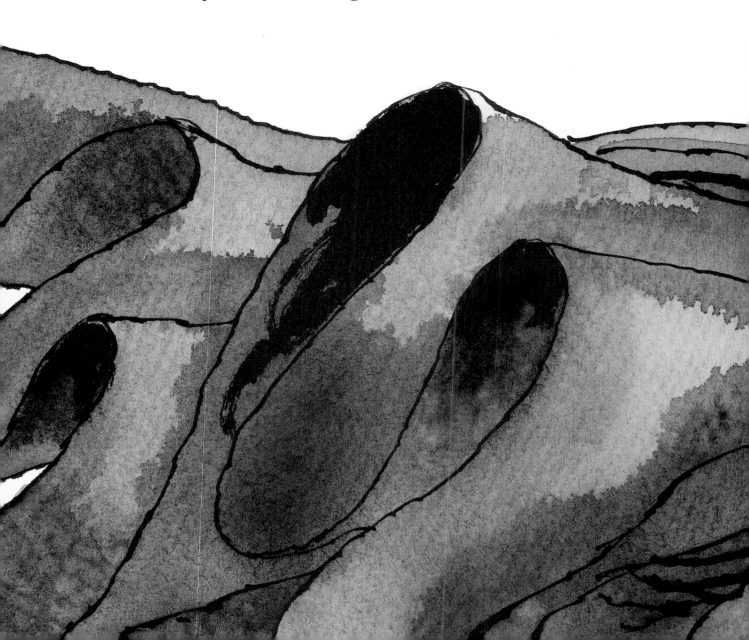

As time went on the standard of living improved, ev
Many of them moved out of the hills and into castl
east of the sun and west of the moon.

the trolls.
away over the mountains,

But the trolls felt kind of lonely living alone, so they took up the habit of kidnapping princesses. They hold them as hostages, until the <u>Ashlad</u>, or some prince, comes along. He cuts off the trolls 1, 2, 3, 6, 9 or even 12 heads, rescues the princess, and in due time gets her and half the kingdom as reward.

As time went even further on,
the small trolls, living in
the hills and under the
ground, became envious
of the Norwegians and
formed their own world,
a copy of the human one,
complete with cattle, farms,
churches, etc., etc., etc.,
They are called
<u>the underground
people</u>.
They are small, not very
beautiful themselves,
but they have
beautiful daughters,
called . . .

. . .<u>Hulder</u>.
She is well equipped up front to lure any
innocent farmboy underground,
where he is bewitched, and must stay
as her husband for ever.

But just as a medal has two sides
so does the hulder.
She has a tail like a cow.

Once in a while a hulder falls so much in love with a boy that she is willing to marry him in a Christian church.
She then loses her tail, and becomes the best wife a man can have.

When the hulder grows older (some 400-500 years) she changes and becomes a <u>Trollkjerring</u>. She is then even able to take her head off and carry it under her arm. Why she developed this peculiar behaviour nobody knows. Maybe just another female whim.

Some of the underground people moved up in the world and into the Norwegians' farms and homes, where they installed themselves as house-gods. They constantly harass the Norwegians and other humans around, but they take good care of the Norwegians' cattle. If you meet a very small and strange person in a Norwegian home, watch out and act with caution. Maybe you just met a <u>Nisse</u>.

To keep the nisse relatively happy,
the Norwegians have to feed him properly.
Every Christmas Eve they set out a big bowl
of porridge in the barn for the nisse.
This scene is often reproduced on
Norwegian Christmas cards, and the nisse
is then called <u>Julenisse</u>.
But remember:
He is a heathen house-god.

If you are attacked by a troll, there are various methods for saving yourself:
1. If you are smart, you can outwit him, because he is not too brilliant . . .

2. But if method 1 fails, you can use your faith and the cross against him . . .

3. But if methods 1 and 2 fail, and you
   have an old muzzle loader and a silver button
   for a bullet . . .

4. But if methods 1, 2, and 3 fail, you can throw steel over his head (or heads) and he will disappear. But be careful before you start throwing any knives around; he could be one of your family.

5. But if methods 1, 2, 3 and 4 fail, your only chance is to run until the sun rises, and the troll will either stop chasing you, or burst.

Ignorant foreigners often ask:
Do the trolls still exist?

Just take a trip into the nearest wood
some dark and stormy night . . .

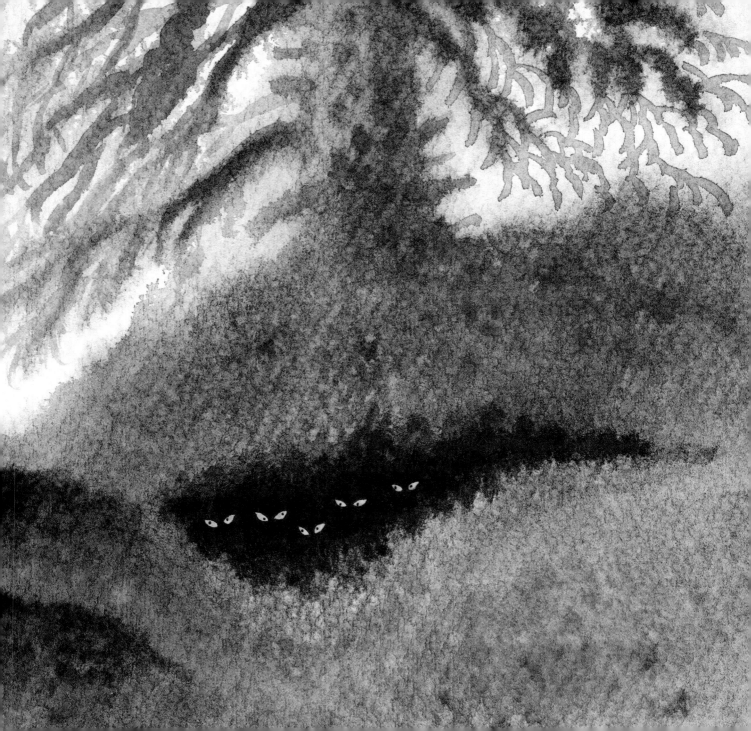

So: Beware. They are watching you!

And maybe if <u>you</u> lose control . . .

TROLLS AND THEIR RELATIVES

Idea and text by: Jan Bergh Eriksen
Drawings by: Per Aase
Printed in Norway by:
Aase Grafiske, Stavanger

ISBN 09-0935-2-5